Cue in to Cloze 2

Cue in to Cloze 2

Graded cloze texts and language activities for Reading Ages 9 to 12

Lynn Hutchinson

Hodder Murray
A MEMBER OF THE HODDER HEADLINE GROUP

Lynn Hutchinson is the writing name of Lynn
Stuart, currently working as a peripatetic specialist
teacher for the Service to Communication
Disordered Children, Northumberland. She
gained a Certificate in Education at Bretton Hall
College of Education, a BA (Open) in Educational
Studies, and a DAES (University of Newcastle-
upon-Tyne) in Child Language and Disability.
She has had many years' experience in a variety
of mainstream and special needs settings.

British Library Cataloguing in Publication Data
Hutchinson, Lynn
    Cue in to cloze 2
    1. Cloze procedure – Study and teaching (Secondary)
    2. Language acquisition – Study and teaching (Secondary)
    I. Title
    428.2

ISBN 978 0340 679 425
First published 1996

Impression number 10
Year 2008 2007

Printed in Great Britain for Hodder Education, the educational
publishing division of Hodder Headline, 338 Euston Road,
an Hachette Livre UK company, London NW1 3BH,
by Hobbs the Printers Ltd, Totton, Hampshire SO40 3WX.

Contents

Introduction

These activity sheets are designed to develop and practise language skills at an increasingly complex level. They have been developed particularly for less able Key Stage 3 pupils, but are also suitable for more able Key Stage 2 pupils. They should interest 11-14 year olds whose written language skills are more like those of 9-12 year olds.

As an indication of reading difficulty the texts have been graded using the (modified) Fog Index. This index takes account of sentence length and the number of polysyllabic words in a passage of 100 words, but not of the type and complexity of sentence structures, or of the difficulty of the content. The index is therefore useful as a guide only and may help provide an entry point. The index should not replace a teacher's judgement.

Each activity starts with a cloze text. This has proved to be a very useful procedure to help develop awareness of sentence structures (syntax) and meaning (semantics). In order to complete the text the pupils take account of both forward- and backward-acting cues so that the completion makes sense. Experience is also given in recognising and becoming comfortable with the tenses of verbs, singularity/plurality, relative clauses, recognising subject and complement, passive sentences, co-ordination and subordination of clauses, pronominal reference and negation.

After each cloze text there are questions and activities which encourage the development of semantic skills: these include locating information, analysis techniques, categorising, summarising, re-organising, inference, prediction and generalisation. The activity sheets are photocopiable and can be used in different ways.

The Cloze

The cloze texts can be completed individually, in pairs or in a group. For instance, pupils can work in groups, each reading a sentence aloud from the cloze text saying 'something' for each deletion. This helps them become aware how much prosody contributes to meaning, and that punctuation is its written counterpart. Individuals and pairs can get together to help complete the final elusive cues.

'Wrong' or inappropriate answers can be used as teaching points. The pupils can be guided to the cues which may be beyond sentence boundaries and therefore disregarded. There are also occasions in which it may be appropriate to pick up a particular point. For example, the cloze texts require single-word responses but contractions are acceptable.

When this arises it could be worth making a brief departure from the text to discuss contractions and identify others. Other possible teaching points might include identifying the subject in a passive sentence, making up sentences with similar grammatical structures and discussing idioms. Because pupils are language users, they usually have an intuitive awareness of what is appropriate: the cloze procedure helps to make explicit what they already know, as well as developing their understanding and awareness of language uses.

The other activities

The first four (single-page) activity sheets consist of a cloze text followed by an 'ANSWER THIS!' activity, in which non-literal open-ended responses such as inference, prediction and generalisation are required. 'ANSWER THIS!' is designed for discussion, which may or may not be teacher-led, and which may or may not develop into written language, as considered appropriate.

The following 24 (double-page) activity sheets consist of a cloze text followed by sets of 'A' and 'B' questions and 'ANSWER THIS!'. The 'A' questions demand fairly literal comprehension skills. Space is given for written sentence responses. There is a good deal of support for both sentence grammar and spelling within the text and questions, so that it is usually possible for all pupils to write correct sentences.

The 'B' questions which follow can be discussed in class first or the pupils can work individually, in pairs or in groups. These activities do not always require sentence answers and are designed to encourage greater interaction with the text, with support to help pupils relate it to their own experience. Space is given for written responses. Sometimes a more able writer can act as a scribe for the group, either presenting the answers orally from notes, or reading out the sentence the group has composed.

Some of these double-page texts also include an 'ANSWER THIS!' activity requiring skills outlined above.

A Key with suggested (though by no means the *only*) answers to the cloze texts, and a (modified) Fog readability guide to the cloze texts, are provided at the end of the book.

Cue in to Cloze 1 precedes this book and is intended particularly for less able 10-13 year olds.

EŪ
GH

On the High Seas

Put a word in each space:

The trading ship didn't have a chance. She _____ left the

East Indies only a few days _____. Trade had been good, and

she _____ heavily laden _____ silks and spices. The

English Court _____ pay well for such luxuries.

The pirate _____ was light and quick. Its sails _____ up

the slightest breeze. It soon outran the _____ ship. The

pirates tied _____ ship alongside, and swarmed aboard.

The crew _____ back, but were quickly beaten.

The goods _____ soon transferred. The crew were _____ up

and taken aboard the _____ ship. The trading vessel was

scuttled, and it sank _____ the waves.

Two days _____ , the crew were rowed _____ a tiny

deserted island. They were _____ one keg of water. The last

_____ they heard were the roars of _____ as the pirate

ship sailed _____ .

answer this!

★ Where was the trading ship going?

★ Give two (or more) possible endings to this story.

Cue in to Cloze 2 *Copyright © 1996 Lynn Hutchinson. Published by Hodder & Stoughton Educational. The publishers grant permission for photocopies of this sheet to be made in the purchasing school or college for use solely in that institution.*

2 Colours

Put a word in each space:

Most people have their own favourite _____. You can

_____ this in the clothes they _____ , as well as in the

colours in _____ homes.

Think of the effect _____ colours. Does red wake you

_____ or send you to sleep? What would the countryside

_____ like if plants and leaves were red? _____ a lot of

blue in a room _____ you feel warm? What colours _____

used most often in bedrooms?

_____ the past, colours have been _____ for healing.

Gemstones such as rubies, sapphires, emeralds and topaz

_____ used. Yellow _____ were worn to help liver

troubles. _____ stones were worn for troubles with the

blood. Green stones were used _____ the eyes. Blue

stones were used _____ a tonic, as well as _____ guard

against evil.

answer this!
- ★ What colours would you use inside an aeroplane?
- ★ Why do you think green colours were used to heal eye
  troubles?

3 Oil

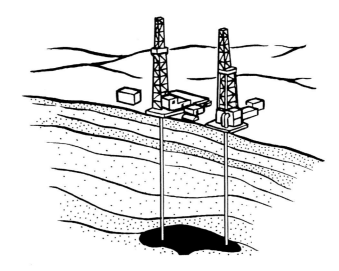

Put a word in each space:

Many plants and small animals _____ in lakes and seas.

_____ they die, they sink _____ the bottom and get covered

_____ mud. If this goes on _____ a long time, a very deep

layer is formed. _____ time, this layer gets buried _____

rocks. The pressure of the _____ turns the remains of these

_____ and animals into oil. Oil we use today is made

_____ plants and _____ which lived millions of _____

ago.

The oil has been trapped _____ layers of rocks. We get

it out _____ drilling down and bringing _____ to the

surface. Oil is not only _____ under the land.

Oil _____ us energy in the form of heat. It is also _____

to make soaps, plastic, nylon and fertilisers.

answer this!

★ Where else is oil found, as well as under the land?

★ How old is the oil we use?

4 The Workhouse

Put a word in each space:

My great-grandfather used to say something _____ puzzled me.

I once asked _____ I could have an ice cream. He said,

'You'll have me _____ the workhouse!'

I asked _____ mum what he meant. She said that a long time

_____ , when my great-grandfather was a boy, there _____

workhouses all over England. They were _____ people who

were too poor or ill to feed themselves. In those _____ if

you could not get a _____ , or you were too ill to _____ ,

your family _____ look after you. If your _____ was

poor, ill or dead, you _____ went to the workhouse or

starved to _____ .

My mum said that poor _____ were frightened that they might

have to _____ there if they had bad luck. Husbands and

wives weren't _____ to see each other ever again. If

_____ weren't already orphans, children were taken away

_____ their parents. People _____ were taken there were

worked almost to death and _____ very little food.

answer this!

* How are the poor, sick and out-of-work cared for these
  days?
* What did Great-grandfather mean about the ice cream
  and the workhouse?

4

⑤ At the Track

 Put a word in each space:

Zach was a keen motorcyclist. He often _____ to the track

on Sundays. His Dad used to _____ him. They would put

the _____ on the car, and the bike on the trailer. His

sister Nadia sometimes _____ too.

This Sunday, Zach got on the _____. He followed the

starting procedure and _____ off. After a while the

engine fluttered. He _____ the bike to have a look. He

_____ at the spark plug. He looked _____ the fuel

gauge. They _____ seemed all right. Zach started

_____ again. The engine still fluttered, _____ he

managed to carry on. Then the _____ cut out and he lost

control. He hit a mud hill and _____ off. The bike fell

on him, hurting his _____. He pulled himself from under

it. Blood was welling _____ his trousers. He tried to

stand _____. He knew straight away his leg _____ too

damaged to kick start the bike.

Then Nadia appeared. She _____ he needed help and ran

back to get _____ father.

B *Now answer these questions in sentences:*

1. What went wrong with the bike first?

   _____

2. What did Zach think might have been wrong with it?

   _____

   _____

3. How was Zach's leg hurt?

   _____

4. What happened to Zach when the engine cut out?

   _____

C *Now answer these questions:*

1. Why do you think they usually went to the track on Sundays?

   _____

2. Why couldn't Zach kick start the bike after the accident?

   _____

3. What do you think would have happened if Nadia hadn't appeared?

   _____

4. How do you think Zach will get back to the car?

   _____

5. What do you think Zach's father will do when he sees Zach?

   _____

answer this!

★ Would an accident like this put you off motor cycling?
   Why, or why not?

5.2

⑥ Leaving

 Put a word in each space:

The cart was laden. The bullocks _____ nervous, and ready

to go. _____ little sisters were crying. My mother ran

_____ of the house.

'He says he's _____ leaving!' she cried.

'He'll be killed _____ he stays!' my father shouted.

'_____ all will if we don't _____ immediately!'

He left the bullocks and ran back _____ the house. A

minute later he _____ , dragging the old man. He bundled

_____ on to the cart. We started off _____ the mountain.

The air was hot and thick _____ ash, and we could hardly

_____ , let alone breathe.

We children plodded along behind the _____ for many hours.

_____ last, we reached the city. There we _____

thousands more people like us who were _____ from the

volcano. We were told of _____ who had not got away in

_____ .

Cue in to Cloze 2 *Copyright © 1996 Lynn Hutchinson. Published by Hodder & Stoughton Educational. The publishers grant permission for photocopies of this sheet to be made in the purchasing school or college for use solely in that institution.*

6.1

B *Now answer these questions in sentences:*

1. Why was the family leaving?

   _____

2. Why do you think the bullocks were nervous?

   _____

3. Who do you think the old man was?

   _____

4. How did the children travel?

   _____

C *Now answer these questions:*

1. Why do you think the old man didn't want to leave?

   _____

   _____

2. Why were people going to the city?

   _____

3. Give two reasons which might have stopped others from getting

   away.

   ★ _____

   ★ _____

answer this!

★ What problems face the family once they get to the city?
★ What problems face the city people when thousands more
   people suddenly arrive?

7 The Miller

 Put a word in each space:

My father's cousin came to visit us _____ Holland. They

hadn't met _____ just before the last war.

She told us _____ her childhood growing up in a windmill,

and _____ hard it had been for _____ mother to manage

after the war.

'_____ happened to your father?' I _____.

'He was taken away during the war, and he _____ came back,'

she said.

'But _____?' I asked.

'He was _____ sending signals by the enemy.'

'Did he _____ a radio?' I asked.

'No, he _____ the sails of the windmill! There _____

many people who didn't _____ the country being occupied by

the Nazis, and my father was _____ of them. He was in the

resistance movement and _____ in the only way he could. We

all _____ to give up something in the _____ for

freedom. My father gave his _____.'

Cue in to Cloze 2 *Copyright © 1996 Lynn Hutchinson. Published by Hodder & Stoughton Educational. The publishers grant permission for photocopies of this sheet to be made in the purchasing school or college for use solely in that institution.*

B *Now answer these questions in sentences:*

1. How long had it been since the cousins last met?

_____

2. What had happened to the miller?

_____

3. Who had taken the miller away?

_____

4. Why was the miller taken away?

_____

C *Now answer these questions:*

1. What had been hard for the miller's wife, and why?

_____

2. Who do you think had found out about the signals, and what would

they have done?

_____

3. Can you suggest how the miller might have used the sails?

_____

4. What can you tell about what sort of man the miller was?

_____

answer this!

★ What do you think the resistance movement was, who
would have been in it, and why?
★ What risks did people in the resistance movement take?

(8) Saved from the Sea

⭐ **A** *Put a word in each space:*

'Can we swim?' asked Ben, looking at the sea.

'Yes, if it's safe,' _____ his uncle.

'I can't _____ any notices. Julie can swim half a

_____ ,' Ben said.

'And Ben can _____ a mile,' Julie said.

The children were soon _____ the water. Some time later

Uncle Bill noticed _____ waving. He _____ back. Then he

realised they weren't waving _____ fun. They were in

trouble. He raced into the _____ and started to swim out.

He was a strong _____ , but how could he _____ them

both?

A woman ran _____ to Aunty Joan. 'It's the current,' she

_____. 'They won't have the strength to swim _____.'

Suddenly Uncle Bill realised he was _____ alone. A man

with a surfboard was swimming _____ him. The man reached

Ben, who grabbed the _____. Uncle Bill reached Julie.

It seemed to take _____ before they got the children

_____ the shore. Aunty Joan flung towels _____ the

shaking children. She hugged _____. Then she turned to

_____ the man with the surfboard. She looked up the _____

and down. She looked _____ the water. He had

completely disappeared.

★ **B** *Now answer these questions in sentences:*

1. What two reasons are there which makes everyone think it is safe for
   the children to go into the water?

   ★ _____

   ★ _____

2. What does the woman know that the family don't?

   _____

3. Why is it likely that the children won't be able to swim back to the
   beach?

   _____

4. What choice does Uncle Bill think he might have to make?

   _____

★ **C** *Now answer these questions:*

1. How is Julie saved?

   _____

2. Why doesn't Uncle Bill have to make a choice?

   _____

3. Why do you think Aunty Joan didn't help to save the children?

   _____

4. Why do you think the children were shaking?

   _____

answer this!

★ How do you explain the appearance and disappearance of
the man?

_____

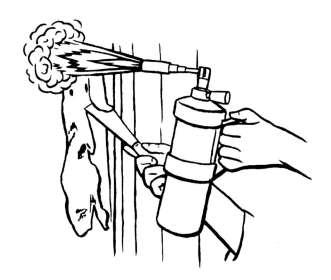

9 Smoke

 Put a word in each space:

It was a hot day. Popi's dad _____ busy. He was burning

the old paint off the woodwork in the house _____ a

blowtorch. When all the paint was _____ he was going to

repaint it. _____ a while he got tired. He decided to

_____ and have some coffee, and went into the _____.

Popi was playing _____ the garden when suddenly she saw

some smoke. There _____ just a few wisps coming _____

the corner of a window, just under the roof. The _____

thickened. Popi threw down her bike and _____ into the

house, calling for her _____. He ran out to see the

smoke, then went for a _____ of water. She ran to the

phone. Then _____ went to help her dad. He had _____

up a ladder and was throwing _____ onto the window frame.

In ten minutes the fire brigade _____. The firemen were

_____ smoke masks. _____ of them ran up the ladder

to check the fire, _____ it was out by then. One of them

_____ into the loft to see if the _____ had spread

inside. Then they went _____.

B *Now answer these questions in sentences:*

1. What did Popi do to help?

   _____

   _____

2. What did Popi's dad do to put out the fire?

   _____

3. What two things did the firemen do?

   _____

   _____

4. Who put out the fire?

   _____

C *Now answer these questions:*

1. What do you think had caused the fire?

   _____

2. How did the fire brigade know there was a fire?

   _____

3. Why do you think they were wearing masks?

   _____

4. Why did a fireman go into the loft?

   _____

answer this!

★ If Popi hadn't seen the fire, what might have happened?

   _____

9.2

(10) Shopping

 Put a word in each space:

It was Friday. Mrs Lacey was _____ her shopping for the

weekend. _____ weekend was special. Her son and _____

family were making a rare visit _____ her.

Mrs _____ was flustered. She hadn't _____ a meal for

anyone else in a _____ time.

In the supermarket, Mrs Lacey _____ slowly down the

aisles. She _____ at all the shelves. They might _____

soup, she thought. She popped a _____ into her basket.

Then she thought that might _____ be enough, and added

_____ tin. She stopped _____ the cheese counter. She'd

better _____ a little more than her usual _____ of

Cheddar. So it went on.

_____ Mrs Lacey got to the _____ , she was surprised at

the amount of food in her _____. She was shocked at _____

much the _____ came to. Worst of _____ , she was

distressed to find she hadn't _____ money in her purse.

(10.1)

B *Now answer these questions in sentences:*

1. Why was Mrs Lacey flustered?

_____

2. What can you tell about Mr Lacey?

_____

3. What can you tell about the rest of Mrs Lacey's family?

_____

4. Why does Mrs Lacey become distressed?

_____

C *Now answer these questions:*

1. Why was Mrs Lacey surprised at the amount of food in her basket?

_____

_____

2. Name at least two things Mrs Lacey could do when she found she hadn't enough money?

★ _____

★ _____

3. What could Mrs Lacey have done before and during her shopping trip to stop herself getting into this embarrassing position?

_____

_____

answer this!

★ What can you tell about Mrs Lacey's lifestyle?

(11) The Arrest

⭐ **A** *Put a word in each space:*

As he drove through the town, Dennis checked his speed.

Then he looked _____ the clock. He had made good

_____ since leaving the docks. He _____ being

careful because he didn't _____ to be caught speeding on

his first trip _____ a container lorry.

He glanced _____ the mirror. A blue flashing light could

be _____ in the distance. Then he _____ the

siren. For a moment he _____ it must be the police

coming after him! Then he realised it was _____ a

silver car which was being _____ down the middle of the

road.

Quickly, _____ the silver car got too close, Dennis

turned the _____ wheel, making the lorry jack-knife

_____ the road. The _____ car couldn't get past and

screeched to a _____. Two men jumped _____. By this

time the _____ car had pulled up and their escape was

_____. Passers-by helped _____ jumping on one of the

men, while the police caught the _____ one. They were

_____ handcuffed and led away.

(11.1)

B *Now answer these questions in sentences:*

1. Why did Dennis check his speed?

_____

2. Where had Dennis collected his load?

_____

3. What sort of vehicle was he driving?

_____

4. What was special about this day for Dennis?

_____

5. Do the cars approach the lorry from the front or from behind?

_____

C *Now answer these questions:*

1. Why did Dennis jack-knife the lorry?

_____

_____

2. Why couldn't the men turn round and drive away?

_____

3. How did passers-by help the police?

_____

4. What will Dennis have to do now?

_____

answer this!

★ Why do police cars use blue flashing lights and sirens?
★ Why might the police have been chasing the silver car?

_____

(12) In a Rush

 A Put a word in each space:

Royston was always in a hurry. He liked to do things _____

didn't take long. He teased _____ sister Maria when she

took _____ knitting. He couldn't imagine doing something

which _____ take weeks to finish! Royston _____

football most of all. He _____ in a team.

Royston's dad used to mend _____ bike for him. Then his

dad moved out. _____ left Royston a book called *Look*

After Your Bike.

One day, Royston noticed his tyre was _____. He realised

he had a puncture. However, he _____ have enough time to

mend it straight _____. He _____ to mend it

before the match on Sunday afternoon.

On Sunday he didn't _____ mending the puncture _____

after dinner. He got the patch on _____ quickly as

possible, and the tyre back _____ the bike.

He set off for the _____. Ten minutes later the _____

was flat again. He realised he wouldn't _____ there in

time. Abdul would be playing _____ his place. Bitterly,

he wheeled his bike _____ home.

Cue in to Cloze 2 Copyright © 1996 Lynn Hutchinson. Published by Hodder & Stoughton Educational. The publishers grant permission for photocopies of this sheet to be made in the purchasing school or college for use solely in that institution.

B *Now answer these questions in sentences:*

1. Why did Royston need to mend his bike?

_____

2. How did Royston know what to do?

_____

3. When did Royston start to mend his bike?

_____

4. Why didn't Royston get to the match?

_____

_____

C *Now answer these questions:*

1. Why do you think Royston's dad gave him a book?

_____

2. What do you think was the time of the kick-off?

_____

3. Why do you think Royston's tyre went flat again?

_____

_____

4. Name two possible consequences of Royston missing the match.

_____

_____

answer this! ★ How could Royston have prevented this from happening?

13 Claystead's Favourite German

⭐ **A** *Put a word in each space:*

The Mayor greeted 'Claystead's Favourite German' last week. He

_____ Herr Erich Baden of Bonn, in Germany. _____ was

Herr Baden's first visit to Claystead _____ the Second World

War.

Then, he _____ a young man in the German Air Force.

_____ the 19th March, 1943, he was on a scouting mission.

Somehow he _____ the other planes. His plane developed

engine _____ and lost height. Herr Baden knew he _____

have to land quickly. One of the engines _____ into flames.

It was going to be a _____ landing. He got ready to

_____.

Then, _____ Baden realised he was coming _____ on to a

village.

Risking his _____ life, he stayed in the plane. Only

_____ it was clear of the buildings did he jump_____. He

landed in the Claystead _____ yard. The _____ crashed

into the field behind the school. Herr Baden _____ both

legs. Thanks to _____ brave action, no one in the village

was _____.

B *Now answer these questions in sentences:*

1. When was Herr Baden flying over the village?

   _____

2. Where were the other planes?

   _____

3. What was Herr Baden meant to be doing?

   _____

4. Why was Herr Baden flying over the village?

   _____

C *Now answer these questions:*

1. What were the possible consequences of Herr Baden staying

   in the plane?

   _____

   _____

2. Did Herr Baden suffer by staying in the plane?

   _____

3. Why did Herr Baden wait before he jumped out of the plane?

   _____

   _____

answer this!

★ Describe what you would have seen if you were a child playing in the school yard.

★ If you were Herr Baden, what would you have done?

14 Edith

 Put a word in each space:

Edith was an old lady _____ lived in a cottage _____ our house. She was thought to _____ quite mad, though harmless. She could often be _____ sitting in an old pushchair _____ the side of the road. She was _____ at dawn, winter and summer. She _____ often be heard shouting to someone _____ the time. Sometimes she asked for the _____ of the week.

The strangest thing was _____ clothes. _____ was nearly eighty, and was bent nearly double. She _____ huge old men's boots, tied on _____ string. Round her legs she _____ newspaper and polythene. Her clothes appeared to be _____ up of layers of bin bags and newspapers. She wore a blue polythene sheet over her _____ which she used as a cloak.

People _____ her proper clothes, of course. She burnt them or _____ them out of the window.

B *Now answer these questions in sentences:*

1. Why do you think Edith used a pushchair?

   _____

2. What time did Edith get up in June?

   _____

3. How do you know Edith didn't wear a watch?

   _____

4. Why do you think people gave her clothes?

   _____

   _____

C *Now answer these questions:*

1. Why was a polythene cloak specially sensible for Edith?

   _____

2. Why do you think Edith got rid of clothes people gave her?

   _____

3. In what ways was Edith's choice of clothes sensible?

   _____

4. Why did people think Edith was mad?

   _____

answer this!

★ Compare Edith's life with that of an old lady in a Home for the Elderly. Write down the advantages of living like Edith, then the advantages of being in a Home.

★ Edith did go into a Home eventually. Why do you think that was?

(15) Anting

 Put a word in each space:

Many birds can _____ seen anting. Anting is _____ a bird

picks up an _____ in its beak, and rubs it _____ its

feathers. Sometimes a bird allows lots of ants to _____

through its plumage.

For a long _____ no one knew why birds _____ this. Then

it _____ found that ants give off a chemical _____

formic acid. Many _____ , including mites and lice, hate

this substance. People now think that _____ go anting to

keep _____ clean.

Now something else _____ been found out about anting. Some

ants also _____ off an antibiotic. _____ antibiotic

kills some germs. Perhaps the birds are _____ themselves

healthy as well _____ clean!

Do you think birds _____ why they go anting?

⭐ **B** *Now answer these questions in sentences:*

1. What is formic acid?

   _____

2. Where do birds find formic acid?

   _____

3. Why do birds want formic acid in their feathers?

   _____

4. What do antibiotics do?

   _____

5. Where do birds get their antibiotics?

   _____

⭐ **C** *Now answer these questions:*

1. What don't mites and lice like about ants?

   _____

2. What can germs do to living creatures?

   _____

3. What two ways are there of anting?

   _____

   _____

4. What do you think an ant does when a bird picks it up?

   _____

answer this!

★ How do you think the birds know what is good for them?

_____

15.2

A *Put a word in each space:*

'When I started in the pit, miners like me _____ for nine

shillings a day. It wasn't much _____ than the dole, but

at least it was a _____. _____ weren't many of them

before the war.' The old _____ stopped.

'If you worked six days a _____ , that means you were

earning _____ than three pounds! Was it a dangerous

job in those _____?' asked Ashley.

'Every day we'd go _____ the pit knowing that we could

_____ that day. Have you _____ of Gresford, where

they had the _____ disaster? 265 men were _____ on

one day. That was _____ of fire damp. Gas levels had

built up, until the _____ eventually exploded. The fire was

so _____ that they had to seal _____ the shafts. They

left the bodies _____ there. Everyone knew something was

_____ to happen. It was the same everywhere. Risks were

_____ all the time.'

'Why did you take _____?' asked Ashley.

'Coal production had _____ be kept up at all costs. If we'd

protested, we'd have _____ our jobs,' explained the

_____ man.

'Instead, 265 men at Gresford lost their _____!' replied

Ashley. 'All for nine shillings a _____.'

★ **B** **Now answer these questions in sentences:**

1. Why did the old man reckon work was better than the dole?

_____

2. Why did they leave the bodies down the pit at Gresford?

_____

3. What would be the effect of sealing the shafts after the explosion
at Gresford?

_____

_____

★ **C** **Now answer these questions:**

1. Why did the miners take risks?

_____

_____

2. What would have been the effect on the *mineowners* if coal
production had fallen?

_____

_____

3. What would have been the effect on the *miners* if coal production
had fallen?

_____

_____

answer this!

★ How did the miners suffer as a result of the mineowners
being powerful?

(17) Mountain Rescue

A *Put a word in each space:*

Mountain Rescue teams save _____ who get into trouble

_____ the mountains. The people who get into trouble are

often people _____ do not know how to behave on

mountains. Sometimes _____ are people who are skilled

mountaineers, _____ who still have _____

accident. An accident can _____ to anyone.

On high _____ the weather can change _____

quickly. It is easy to get _____ in snow and mist. If

you are _____ prepared, and don't know _____ to

do, you will soon suffer _____ exposure. This is

_____ the wind and the cold chill your _____.

Death can follow quite quickly.

Some Mountain _____ teams in other countries _____

German Shepherd dogs. This is why. Tests _____ shown

that when a man was buried _____ 25 square metres of

snow it _____ an average of 28 minutes for a person to

_____ him. If the person _____ a metal detector,

on average it took 9 _____ to find him. It took a

_____ just half a minute. A trained dog _____

certainly speed up rescue work.

B *Now answer these questions in sentences:*

1. What is a Mountain Rescue team for?

   _____

2. What is the danger from weather on high mountains?

   _____

3. What is exposure?

   _____

4. What is the worst thing that can happen if you suffer from exposure?

   _____

C *Now answer these questions:*

1. What sort of things might people do wrong if they don't know how
   to behave on high mountains?

   _____

   _____

2. What is the *slowest* way to find a person buried in snow?

   _____

3. What is the *quickest* way to find a person buried in snow?

   _____

4. Why is speed important in Mountain Rescue work?

   _____

answer this!

★ Why do you think a trained dog is so good at finding
  buried people?

★ What other dogs help people, and how?

18 Forest Fire

 A ⭐ *Put a word in each space:*

When a forest burns, the burning wood _____ a noise like

the crackling of dry _____. Birds _____ down the

wind before the flames. Scared animals _____ to rush

away from the spreading heat. _____ that fall are

trampled down _____ others, or are overcome by smoke.

_____ the flames reach fresh trees they ignite _____

bursts of hisses and crackles. The _____ smells strongly

of burning wood, and sometimes also of _____ fur and

meat.

The animals _____ can escape make for the river.

_____ will tumble down the banks, or _____

themselves into the water. To cross the _____ to safety

they have to _____ against the current. In the river

they are _____ from the flames, but _____ from the

sparks leaping _____ the burning bank, or the charred logs

_____ fall into the river. Dead or exhausted

_____ are carried helplessly downstream.

⭐ **B** *Now answer these questions in sentences:*

1. What happens to the animals which fall as they run away?

_____

_____

2. Why does the smoke smell of meat?

_____

3. What are animals in the water safe from?

_____

4. What are the animals in the water *not* safe from?

_____

5. Why do you think the birds fly before the flames?

_____

⭐ **C** *Now answer these questions:*

1. What sounds would you hear in a burning forest?

_____

2. Why do the animals make for the river, and how do you think they

   know that is the best thing to do?

_____

_____

3. Think of as many events as you can which could cause a forest fire.

_____

answer this!

★ How will the forest be different after a fire?

★ Some people believe that a forest fire is not all bad.
   What could be good about it?

18.2

(19) The Rock Concert

⭐ A   Put a word in each space:

The doors opened at _____. Jerome and Jeff pushed

forward because they _____ to get close to the stage. It

was the first live rock _____ they had been to. Excitement

built _____ as the hall became packed. Then the first

_____ came on stage and the _____ started.

The heat soon became unbearable. Jerome wondered _____ he

would survive until the _____. Once, he _____ his

hands above his head to _____. It was so crowded he

couldn't get _____ down for ten minutes. Then Jeff, who

was not very tall, decided to _____ to get a better view.

The _____ suddenly surged. He couldn't get _____ feet

back on the ground _____ the crowd moved again. Then one

_____ climbed onto the stage. He was thrown back _____

the crowd. He had to crawl to the side on his _____ and

knees, right over people's heads and _____ , before he

could get _____.

B *Now answer these questions in sentences:*

1. Why couldn't Jerome get his hands down?

_____

2. What did Jeff have to wait for?

_____

3. Why did the fan have to crawl to the side?

_____

4. What do you think makes it so hot?

_____

C *Now answer these questions:*

1. Why do you think Jerome and Jeff wanted to be near the front?

_____

2. What do you think Jerome means when he wonders if he will survive?

_____

3. Some fans try to climb on the stage and jump off into the crowd.
The crowd passes the fans over their heads to the side. They call this
'surfing'. Why is it dangerous?

_____

_____

answer this!

★ Imagine you were Jerome or Jeff. Think about the sounds,
smells, sights and feelings you experienced. What
describing words would you use to tell someone about the
evening?

(20) The Chance

 A ★ *Put a word in each space:*

Jud had made up his _____. He was definitely going to go.

_____ was the only chance he was _____ to have to save

the family _____ their poverty. When he went, at least

_____ would be one less mouth to feed. When he _____

back, their luck would have changed.

He said _____ to his family. Jud did not _____ it, but he

was one of 100,000 men _____ left to go to California that

year. Many others had also _____ the newspaper reports of

gold. They were all _____ for the lucky strike.

It took Jud twenty weeks _____ walk to the _____ fields.

Then he headed north _____ the river flowing from the

_____. He found a likely looking _____ and staked his

claim. He did this _____ cutting down _____ to make

stakes. Then he marked a piece of _____ with the stakes.

Then began the hard _____ of digging and washing the soil

in the _____.

B *Now answer these questions in sentences:*

1. Why did Jud decide to go?

   _____

2. How did people know about the gold in California?

   _____

3. How did Jud stake his claim?

   _____

4. Why was it useful to have a river nearby?

   _____

C *Now answer these questions:*

1. What does the fact that 20,000 men went to California in one year tell you about life in America then?

   _____

   _____

2. What is a lucky strike?

   _____

3. Only a few people would strike gold. What do you think would happen to the rest?

   _____

4. Do you think Jud's decision was a good or bad thing for the family? Why?

   _____

answer this!

★ How is looking for gold like the Lottery?

   _____

21 The Old House

 A *Put a word in each space:*

The dream was vivid. Every detail _____ clear. There was

a large house _____ windows on three floors, a porch

with a round window _____ it and roses growing round the

door.

Steve _____ up. Later he could still _____ very

clearly what the house _____ like, although he couldn't

remember anything _____ about the dream. The same dream

came to _____ a few more times, then stopped _____

the years went by.

Years later, when Steve _____ a soldier, he was _____

with his detachment to guard some prisoners _____ war.

The prisoners were to _____ kept at an old hall

in the country until the _____ of the war. As the

detachment _____ up the drive for the first _____ ,

Steve had _____ first view of the hall. It had three

_____ , a round window above the _____ , and

_____ round the door.

★B Now answer these questions in sentences:

1. What part of the dream does Steve remember for some time?

_____

2. What does Steve notice about the windows?

_____

3. What does Steve notice about the door?

_____

4. How many flights of stairs must there be, at the least?

_____

5. When do you think Steve stopped having the dream?

_____

★C Now answer these questions:

1. Why do you think Steve became a soldier?

_____

2. When do you think this happened?

_____

3. Where was Steve sent until the end of the war?

_____

4. What was the detachment's job until the end of the war?

_____

answer this! ★ What do you think you would feel if you were Steve, when you first saw the house?

(22) The Cottage

 A **Put a word in each space:**

Dear Visitor,

This is how to find the _____. Drive up the single

track _____ from the village for one mile. Stop _____

the telephone box next _____ the bridge. Go through the

_____ on the right with the sign 'PLEASE _____ THE

GATE' on it. Drive for half a mile through the fields

_____ you reach another gate.

Follow the track _____ the brow of the hill. _____

carefully, because on the left there _____ a steep drop

to the river. You can _____ the cottage nestled into the

hills _____ the last quarter of a mile.

The cottage is an _____ slate miner's cottage, with a

walled _____ in front. The wall is to _____ out the

sheep _____ you will find everywhere. The _____ of

the cottage is on the front _____ , *Tyn-y-cornel'*, which

means 'house in the corner'. _____ will find the key

_____ the mat. Enjoy your _____!

Cue in to Cloze 2 *Copyright © 1996 Lynn Hutchinson. Published by Hodder & Stoughton Educational. The publishers grant permission for photocopies of this sheet to be made in the purchasing school or college for use solely in that institution.* (22.1)

B *Now answer these questions in sentences:*

1. About how far is the cottage from the village?

_____

2. How do you know which telephone box to stop at?

_____

3. Can you see the cottage from the telephone box?

_____

4. On which side of the road is the gate with a notice?

_____

C *Now answer these questions:*

1. When should you drive extra carefully, and why?

_____

_____

2. What can you tell about the history of the cottage?

_____

3. What clues are there to tell you what the cottage is used for now?

_____

_____

4. Which country do you think the cottage is in, and why?

_____

answer this!

★ How do you think the farmers around 'Tyn-y-cornel' make
   their living?

★ Why do you think the cottage is called 'Tyn-y-cornel'?

(23) The Little Cat

 Put a word in each space:

The little cat _____ exhausted. All _____ wanted

was somewhere warm, somewhere _____ food, somewhere she

could stay. She _____ her way through the cold, wet

bushes. Suddenly she _____ a hiss. She stopped,

cowering with _____. Just ahead of her, _____ a

partly fallen fence post, was a large tom _____.

He was sheltering in a sort of cave _____ of dry grass.

He looked at her, sniffed, then leapt _____ through the

undergrowth. She didn't _____ what to do, so she

_____ him at a distance. He led her _____ a door,

outside which was a _____ of milk and some scraps

_____ food. He drank, ate, then moved _____. She

crept up and finished the _____ and _____.

The door opened. In a flash the _____ cat disappeared

into the dark. The _____ cat was dazzled _____ the

light. Two small hands _____ down, lifted her up, and

_____ her indoors. She _____ understand the words,

but she knew that for a little _____ , at least, she

would be _____.

Cue in to Cloze 2 *Copyright © 1996 Lynn Hutchinson. Published by Hodder & Stoughton Educational. The publishers grant permission for photocopies of this sheet to be made in the purchasing school or college for use solely in that institution.*

(23.1)

B *Now answer these questions in sentences:*

1. What time of day is this?

_____

2. What time of year is this?

_____

3. Why do you think the tom cat hisses?

_____

4. Why does the little cat cower with fear?

_____

5. How does the tom cat manage to stay dry?

_____

C *Now answer these questions:*

1. What had made the little cat exhausted?

_____

_____

2. Why do you think there is food and drink outside the door?

_____

_____

3. Why did the tom cat leave some food and milk?

_____

_____

answer this!

★ How did the little cat get exhausted? Write a beginning to this story.

★ Give three endings to this story.

(24) Hijack

 A *Put a word in each space:*

'This is Linda Hofmann. Here is the latest report _____ the hijack.' Linda kept glancing _____ the windows of the phone box. The _____ was still on the runway. When she had finished _____ the news through to her newspaper, she _____ back.

'What's going on?' she _____ another reporter.

'Still no agreement,' was the _____. 'The hijackers _____ release the passengers unless the prisoners are released. The authorities won't _____ the prisoners they've asked for.'

Just then they saw a _____ on the plane open. Five figures _____ down the steps from the aircraft. Three of _____ were children.

'Any more?' _____ asked an official.

'That's all,' he replied. 'The _____ 81 stay. If they _____ any trouble they'll be killed. One _____ one,' the hijackers said, until their demands _____ met.'

Linda could see food being loaded _____ the plane.

'At least it _____ as if they're still talking,' she _____.

B *Now answer these questions in sentences:*

1. What do you think Linda's job is?

   _____

2. What do the hijackers want?

   _____

3. What do the hijackers threaten if they don't get what they want?

   _____

4. Why do you think the authorities are giving them food?

   _____

C *Now answer these questions:*

1. Why might you release some of the passengers if you were a hijacker?

   _____

   _____

2. Why do you think the authorities are refusing the hijackers' demands?

   _____

   _____

3. What would you do now if you were in authority?

   _____

   _____

answer this! ★ Assume you were a passenger who survived the hijack. Give your own account of what happened.

24.2

(25) Windfalls

 _A_ ***Put a word in each space:***

Did you know that _____ hundreds of years there have been

reports of strange things falling _____ the sky? The most

common reports are of showers _____ frogs, toads and

fish. Sometimes they are _____ when they fall to earth,

and sometimes _____ are alive.

In the Middle Ages _____ people believed that the seeds

_____ frogs and toads lay in the soil just waiting

_____ a heavy burst of rain. Then the seeds would _____

and the ground would soon be _____ in frogs and toads.

However, it has been proved _____ they really can come

from the _____. They were seen _____ onto umbrellas

in Birmingham in June 1954.

The most common _____ is that a freak wind lifts the

creatures into the _____. We know that _____ a

tornado passes over water it sucks _____ the water and

all that is in it. It becomes a waterspout. The _____

spirals upwards. Then, maybe a few miles _____ , frogs

and fish are rained _____ , much to the surprise of any

people _____ beneath!

B *Now answer these questions in sentences:*

1. What are the most common things to fall from the sky?

   _____

2. Some of the creatures are still alive. What does that mean?

   _____

3. Is the weather wet or dry when these creatures fall?

   _____

4. What goes up with the water in a waterspout?

   _____

C *Now answer these questions:*

1. What is a waterspout?

   _____

   _____

2. How do the fish and frogs get from one place to another?

   _____

   _____

3. What can you tell about a tornado from this passage?

   _____

   _____

   _____

answer this! ★ Why do you think people were ready to believe frogs and
toads came from seeds in the ground?

(26) Great White Shark

A ⭐ *Put a word in each space:*

Here are some facts _____ the most dangerous shark of all,

the great white shark:

- they can _____ up to 12 metres long;

- an adult can _____ 9,000 kilos;

- they swim _____ nearly 40 kilometers an hour;

- they _____ smell one drop of blood in 10 million

  drops of sea _____;

- they can hear for hundreds of metres _____ organs

  inside their bodies;

- their _____ are better at seeing shapes than details,

  and _____ shine in the dark.

The sharks have a sensitive part on the sides of _____

bodies called a *lateral line*. From the vibrations _____

this lateral line a shark can _____ where something is, it's

distance and how fast it _____ moving.

Great _____ sharks have to swim all the time. They need

lots _____ oxygen to stay alive, so have _____ keep

water flowing through their gills. They are also _____

heavy they would sink if they stopped _____.

The first baby shark to hatch eats up all the _____ eggs.

Then it swims away in _____ its mother eats it.

B *Now answer these questions in sentences:*

1. What is the same about a shark's eyes and a cat's eyes?

   _____

2. Which part of a shark's body picks up vibrations?

   _____

3. Where do the sharks find oxygen?

   _____

4. Where are the shark's ears?

   _____

5. When do sharks sleep?

   _____

C *Now answer these questions:*

1. What three things can a shark tell from vibrations in the water?

   ★ _____

   ★ _____

   ★ _____

2. Why do sharks swim all the time?

   _____

   _____

3. How does a shark know when someone is injured?

   _____

   _____

answer this!

★ Which *land* animal do you think is most like a shark?

★ Which creature do you know of that is *least* like a shark?

27 The Cat's Name

⭐ A **Put a word in each space:**

'Can you bring the cat _____ the surgery at

4 o'clock?' _____ the vet's receptionist.

'Yes,' said Yasmin.

'And what is the cat's _____?'

'Er.... Amnesia,' _____ replied, a bit embarrassed. 'It's

the word for _____ you've lost your memory.'

Later, at the _____ , the receptionist asked, 'How did your

_____ get a name like Amnesia?'

Yasmin laughed. 'Well, we _____ think of a name she

would respond to at first. Then _____ mum brought a book

home from the _____. It was about some children _____

find a cat, and they _____ to guess its name. Then one of

_____ says, "Perhaps it's _____ amnesia." The cat

miaows. At the _____ they find it's called *Caesar*.'

'What _____ that got to do with _____ cat?' asked the

receptionist.

'Well, I _____ up the book and read the _____ aloud.

It was called *A Cat Called Amnesia*. Our cat pricked up her

_____ and miaowed. That's _____ we've called her ever

since.'

Cue in to Cloze 2 Copyright © 1996 Lynn Hutchinson. Published by Hodder & Stoughton Educational. The publishers grant permission for photocopies of this sheet to be made in the purchasing school or college for use solely in that institution.

B *Now answer these questions in sentences:*

1. Where did the receptionist work?

_____

2. What does 'amnesia' mean?

_____

3. What was the book called?

_____

4. What was the real name of the cat in the book?

_____

C *Now answer these questions:*

1. Why do you think the cat's name surprised the receptionist?

_____

2. Why do you think Yasmin felt embarrassed explaining the cat's name?

_____

3. Why do you think one of the children in the book thought the cat might have amnesia?

_____

4. Why do you think Caesar miaowed when he heard the word 'amnesia'?

_____

answer this!
★ Why do you think Yasmin's cat miaowed when she heard the name Amnesia?
★ Why did Yasmin's family call their cat Amnesia?

28 The Sahara Desert

 A *Put a word in each space:*

Of all the deserts in the world, the Sahara _____ is the

most well known. The word 'sahara' comes _____ the Arab

word 'emptiness'. The Sahara stretches _____ three and a

half million square miles. _____ is mainly sand and

rock. Only part of the desert _____ sand-dunes. They are

blown about by the _____ and keep changing their shape.

In the middle of the _____ desert are rocky mountains.

Some of these _____ to be volcanoes.

People crossing the desert _____ from one oasis to

another. An oasis is formed _____ there is some water.

Date palms, orange, lemon and lime _____ grow there. The

people who live there also _____ vegetables.

At one time _____ camels could cross the Sahara. That is

_____ they can store enough food and water in their bodies

to _____ for weeks. Now, the desert can be crossed

_____ vehicles. As each settlement is 200-300 miles

_____ , a breakdown can be _____ .

28.1

B *Now answer these questions in sentences:*

1. What does the word 'Sahara' mean?

_____

2. How big is the Sahara desert?

_____

3. What is in the middle of the Sahara?

_____

4. How do we know it is windy in the Sahara?

_____

C *Now answer these questions:*

1. Why do you think the Arabs chose the name for this desert?

_____

2. What did the mountains in the middle of the desert used to be?

_____

3. What is an oasis?

_____

4. Why are camels ideal for crossing the desert?

_____

answer this!

★ Think about vehicles crossing the desert. What sort of vehicles would be most suitable? What could be the consequences of a breakdown? How could you reduce the risks? Would you prefer to cross the desert by camel or vehicle?

Key

1 On the High Seas

had, before/previously, was, with, would, ship, picked, trading, their, fought, were, tied, pirate, beneath/below, later, to, given, thing, laughter, away

2 Colours

colours, see, wear/buy, their, of, up, look/be, Does/Will, make, are, In, used, were, stones, Red, for, as, to

3 Oil

live, When, to, with/in, for, In/With/Over, under/by, rocks, plants, from/of, animals, years, between/under/below/beneath, by, it, found, gives, used

4 The Workhouse

which, if, in, my, ago, were, for, days, job, work, would, family, either, death, people, go, allowed, they, from, who, given/had

5 At the Track

went, take, trailer, came, bike, set/started, stopped, looked, at, both, off, but, engine/motor, fell, leg, through, up, was, realised/saw, their

6 Leaving

were, My, out, not, if, We, go/leave, into/to, appeared/emerged, him, down, with, see, cart/bullocks, At, met/found/saw, fleeing, those/some/many/others, time

7 The Miller

from, since, about/of, how, her, What, asked, never, why, caught/found, have/use, used, were, like/want, one, helped/fought, had/have, fight/struggle, life

8 Saved from the Sea

said/answered/replied, see, mile, swim, in, them, waved, for, water/sea, swimmer, save/rescue, up, said, back, not, beside, surfboard, ages, (on)to, round, them, thank, beach, at/in/towards

9 Smoke

was, with, off, After, go/stop, house/kitchen, in, were, from, smoke, ran, father/dad, bucket, she, climbed, water, came/arrived, wearing, One, but, went/climbed, fire/flames, away/back

10 Shopping

doing, This, his, to, Lacey, made/cooked/prepared/got, long, walked, looked, have/like, tin, not, another, at, buy/get, piece/packet, When, checkout, basket, how, bill, all, any/enough

11 The Arrest

at, time, was, want, with/driving, in/at, seen, heard, thought, chasing/after, driven, before, steering, across, silver, halt, out, police, blocked/impossible, by, other, both

12 In a Rush

which, his, up, would/might, liked, played/was, his, He, flat, didn't, away, decided, start, until, as, on, match, tyre, get, in, back

13 Claystead's Favourite German

is, This/It, since, was, On, lost, problems/trouble, would, burst, crash/dangerous, parachute/jump, Herr, down, own, after/when, out/clear, School, plane, broke/hurt/lost, his, hurt/killed/injured

14 Edith

who, near, be, seen, at, out/there, could, for, day, her, Edith/She, wore, with, wrapped/wore, made, shoulders/head, gave, threw

15 Anting

be, when, ant, into/in/through, march/crawl, time, did, was, called, pests/insects, birds, themselves, has, give, This/The, keeping, as, know

16 Nine Shillings a Day

worked, more/better, job, There, man/miner, week, less, days, down/to, die, heard, pit/great/mining, killed, because, gas/mine, bad/fierce, up, down, going, taken, risks, to, lost, old, lives, day

17 Mountain Rescue

people, on/in, who, they, but, an, happen, mountains, very, lost, not, what, from, when, body, Rescue, use/have, have, in/under, took, find, used, minutes, dog, can/will

18 Forest Fire

makes, paper, fly, try, Those, by, As/When, with, air/wind/forest, burning, which, They, throw, river/water, swim, safe, not, from, which, animals

19 The Rock Concert

last, wanted, concert, up, band/group, music, if/whether, end, put/held/lifted, clap/wave, them, jump, crowd, his, until, fan/person, into, hands, shoulders, down

20 The Chance

mind, This/It, going/likely, from, there, came/got, goodbye, know, who, heard/read, hoping, to, gold, up/along, hills/mountains, place/spot, by, trees, land, work/labour, river

21 The Old House

was, with, above, woke, remember, looked/was, else/more, him, as, became, sent, of, be, end, came/marched, time, his, floors, porch, roses

22 The Cottage

cottage, road, by/at, to, gate, CLOSE/SHUT, until, over/to, Drive, is, see, for, old, garden, keep, which, name, gate, You, under, holiday/stay/visit

23 The Little Cat

was, she, with, pushed/made, heard, fear, under/on/beside, cat, made, away/off, know, followed, to, saucer/bowl/dish, of, off/on, food/milk, milk/food, tom, little, by, reached/came, carried/took, didn't, while, warm

24 Hijack

from/on, through, plane, phoning, went/came, asked, reply, won't, release, door, came/walked, them, Linda/they, other, cause/give, by, are, onto, looks, thought/said

25 Windfalls

for, from, of, dead, they, some/most/many, of, for, grow, covered, that, sky, falling, explanation/reason, air/sky, when, up, water, away, down, standing/walking

26 Great White Shark

about, grow, weigh, at, can, water, with/using, eyes, they, their, on, tell, is, white, of, to, so, swimming/moving, other, case

27 The Cat's Name

to, asked, name, Yasmin/she, when, surgery/vet's, cat, couldn't, my, library/shop, who, try, them, got, end, has, your/this, picked, title, ears, what

28 The Sahara Desert

desert, from, for/nearly, It, is, wind, Sahara, used, go/travel/journey, where, trees, grow, only, because, last/walk/travel, by/in, apart, dangerous

Readability Guide

	Text	Average number of words per sentence	Average number of 3-syllable-plus words per 100	For Reading Age
Single-page exercises	1	9	3	9.8
	2	10	3	10.2
	3	12.5	3	11.2
	4	14	3	11.8
Double-page exercises	5	9	1	9.0
	6	7	3	9.0
	7	9.5	1	9.2
	8	7	4	9.4
	9	10.5	1	9.6
	10	9	3	9.8
	11	10.5	2	10.0
	12	10	3	10.2
	13	10.5	3	10.4
	14	9.5	4	10.4
	15	10	4	10.6
	16	11	3	10.6
	17	12.5	2	10.8
	18	12.5	2	10.8
	19	12.5	2	10.8
	20	10	5	11.0
	21	11	4	11.0
	22	12.5	3	11.2
	23	11.5	4	11.2
	24	8	8	11.4
	25	14	2	11.4
	26	12.5	4	11.6
	27	10	7	11.8
	28	10	7	11.8